EASA Private Pilot Licence
Aeroplane
Operational Procedures Revision Guide

ISBN 9781906 559373

Airplan Flight Equipment

This book is intended to be a study aid to the Operational Procedures Theoretical Knowledge element of the EASA PPL (A) course. It does not in any way replace or overrule the instruction you will receive from a flight instructor at an approved or registered training organisation.

Nothing in this publication overrules or supersedes EASA regulations or EU rules and other documents published by a competent authority; the flight manual/pilot's operating handbook for the aircraft being flown; the pilot order book or operations manual; training syllabus; or the general provisions of goodggood good airmanship and safe flying practice.

First Edition 2013

©Copyright 2013 AFE Ltd.

EASA Private Pilot Licence
Aeroplane
Operational Procedures Revision Guide

ISBN 9781906 559373

Airplan Flight Equipment
1a Ringway Trading Estate
Shadowmoss Road
Manchester M22 5LH
Tel: 0161 499 0023
Fax: 0161 499 0298
www.afeonline.com

CONTENTS

Intentionally Left Blank

Operation of Aircraft

The **Pilot In Command** can be defined as the person designated by the operator or the owner as being in command and charged with the safe conduct of the flight. The Pilot In Command is not necessarily the person operating the flight controls, nor necessarily the most experienced pilot in the aircraft. Nevertheless, it is always the Pilot In Command who carries the ultimate responsibility for the safety of the aircraft and everyone in it.

An **Operations Manual** is a manual containing procedures, instructions and guidance for use by operational personnel in the execution of their duties. In practice, it is a document maintained by an aircraft operator which the pilot should refer to regarding the operator's procedures.

A **Flight Manual** is a manual associated with the Certificate of Airworthiness, containing limitations within which the aircraft is to be considered airworthy, together with instructions and information necessary for the flight crew members to safely operate the aircraft. Every individual aircraft with a Certificate of Airworthiness will have its own individual Flight Manual.

For aeroplanes, **Flight Time** is defined as the total time from when an aeroplanes first moves for the purpose of taking off until the moment it finally comes to rest at the end of the flight. This time is sometimes also referred to as 'chock to chock' time.

By ICAO definition, **General Aviation Operation** is an aircraft operation other than commercial air transport or aerial work operation. Commercial air transport involves the transport of passengers or cargo for money; aerial work includes specialised services such as survey, aerial advertising, search and rescue etc.

The following definitions can be used to describe **runway dimensions** and physical characteristics:

Landing distance available (LDA) – the length of the runway suitable for the ground run of an aeroplane landing.

Take-off run available (TORA) – the length of runway suitable for the ground run of an aeroplane taking off.

Accelerate-stop distance available (ASDA) – the length of the take-off run available plus the length of any stopway.

Take-off distance available (TODA) – the length of the take-off run available plus the length of the clearway available.

Stopway – an area beyond the runway which can be safely used for stopping an aircraft in the event of an aborted take-off.

Clearway – an area beyond the runway, free of obstructions and under the control of the airport authorities, over which an aircraft can make part of its initial climb after take-off.

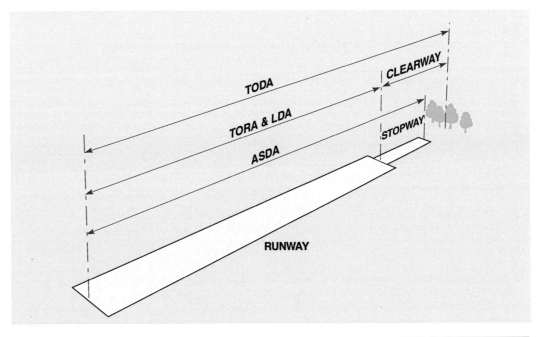

A runway holding point can be marked with one of more of the following:

Holding point 'boards' at the side of the taxiway and runway

A set of solid and broken yellow lines painted across the taxiway

A line of steady red lights across the taxiway (the 'stop bar')

Flashing amber 'Runway Guard Lights' next to or across the taxiway

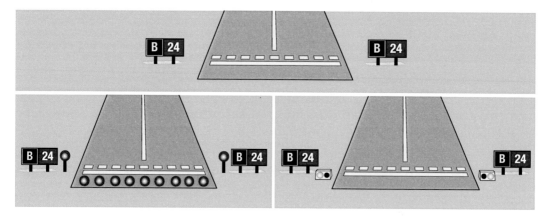

At a controlled aerodrome, the holding point must not be crossed without ATC clearance, and even then only after making a good lookout for aircraft on or approaching the runway. Regardless of ATC clearance, a pilot should not cross an illuminated stop bar.

Ground to Air **Light Signals**:

ATC Light Signals to Aircraft on Ground

STOP	STOP
GET OFF GET OFF	Move clear of runway
GO	You may take-off
OK TAXI OK TAXI	OK to Taxi
COME BACK COME BACK	Return to starting point

ATC Light Signals to Aircraft in the Air

NO	Give way and continue circling
GO AWAY GO AWAY	Do not land here
LAND	You may land
COME BACK COME BACK	Return to this airfield
LAND HERE LAND HERE	Land at this airfield

'Night' can be defined as the hours between the end of evening civil twilight and the beginning of morning civil twilight. Evening civil twilight ends when the centre of the sun's disc is six degrees below the horizon; morning civil twilight begins when the centre of the sun's disc is six degrees below the horizon.

Noise Abatement

Noise abatement procedures normally consist of specific routing on arrival and departure (including the circuit) at a specific airfield. These routing (or avoidance areas) are usually notified in the airfield's entry in the Aeronautical Information Publication (AIP) or commercial flight guide.

Fire and Smoke

A situation involving fire in an aircraft, especially when it is airborne, is a very serious (and very rare) occurrence which requires prompt action by the pilot.

Engine fires on start are most often caused by over-priming the engine – either by over-use of the priming control or by 'pumping' the throttle of an engine fitted with an accelerator pump.

Cabin fires in the air in light aircraft are most often caused by some kind of electrical failure and may be characterised by white smoke and an 'acrid' smell.

As with any emergency event, the procedures and actions for dealing with a fire should be guided by the aircraft's emergency checklist, as appropriate to the circumstances of the emergency.

Windshear and Microburst

Wind shear is a <u>sudden</u> change of wind velocity and/or direction. Vertical wind shear is a change of horizontal wind direction and/or speed with height, horizontal wind shear is defined as change of horizontal wind direction and/or speed with horizontal distance.

Wind shear, especially at low level, can lead to sudden and significant changes in airspeed and flight path and can represent a serious flight hazard. A sudden change in headwind or tailwind component will cause a rapid, and possibly short-lived, change in airspeed and rate of descent or rate of climb.

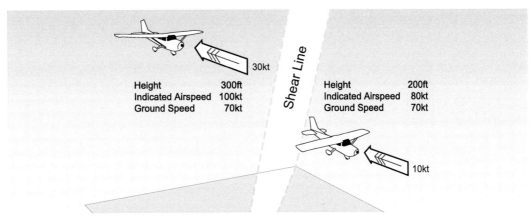

Windshear is most often associated with thunderstorms, but can also occur around particularly active weather fronts, across a temperature inversion and in turbulence caused by strong winds.

A microburst is a powerful localised area of rain-cooled descending air which, after hitting the ground, spreads out in all directions. Microbursts are most often associated with thunderstorms, but can also occur in association with 'virga' – rain evaporating before reaching the ground. A microburst will often involve strong downdraughts and horizontal winds and can cause severe windshear.

A Energy gain
  - increasing headwind
  - Airspeed rising
  - Rate of descent reduced
  - Tendency to go high on glidepath

B Energy loss
  - reducing headwind and downdraught
  - Airspeed falling
  - Rate of descent Increased
  - Tendency to go low on glidepath

C Energy loss
  - Increasing tailwind
  - Airspeed still falling
  - Rate of descent checked by missed approach
  - Success depends on power, height and speed reserves available

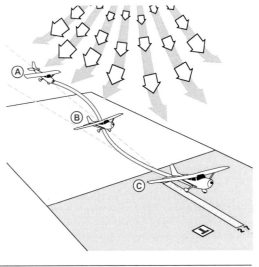

Wake Turbulence

In general terms, **wake turbulence** is a disturbance of the air caused by the passage of an aircraft in flight. Wake turbulence is most often considered to be in the form of vortices generated at the wing tips of a fixed wing aircraft or from the rotors of a helicopter. In the case of a fixed-wing aircraft, wake turbulence is generally considered to exist from the time the nosewheel leaves the ground on take-off until the nosewheel contacts the runway on landing.

The bigger and heavier an aircraft, and the more slowly it is flying, the greater the wake turbulence it will produce. Wake turbulence vortices tend to slowly descend and drift out from the wing tips (or rotor blades) behind an aircraft, so can be avoided by positioning above the aircraft's flightpath. In light crosswind conditions, a wing tip vortex may actually remain stationary or move in the opposite direction to that expected.

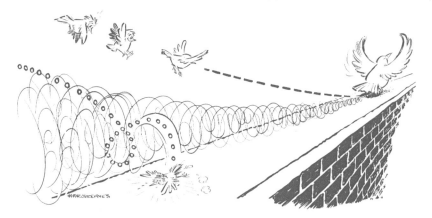

Helicopters produce stronger wake turbulence than aeroplanes of a similar size and weight. It is recommended to remain at a distance of <u>at least</u> three rotor disc diameters from a helicopter in flight to avoid its wake turbulence.

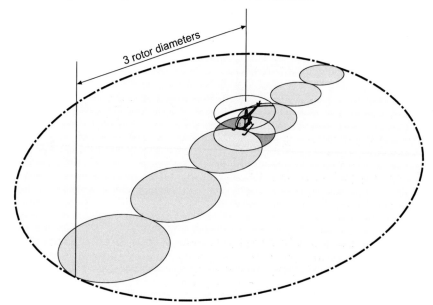

Various minimum times and distances are recommended to separate a following aircraft from a leading one in order to minimise the chances of wake turbulence encounter.

Emergency and Precautionary Landings

A forced landing is a situation where a pilot is required to make an unavoidable landing (or ditching) and there can be a reasonable expectation of no injuries to those in the aircraft or on the surface.

In the event of an engine failure during cruise in a single-engine aircraft, and subject to the circumstances and emergency checklist, the general sequence of actions may include:

- establish best glide airspeed, assess surface wind, select landing area and plan descent pattern;

- check for causes of failure, in particular: fuel controls, carburettor heat/induction air and ignition switches. If appropriate, attempt re-start;

- make appropriate radio call

- carry-out 'committed checks'

In the event of an engine failure over water and beyond gliding distance of land, it may be appropriate to descend at the best glide endurance airspeed (for maximum time airborne) and to contact ATC (including, if appropriate, using the emergency transponder code 7700) at the beginning of the sequence of actions, in order to increase the chances of being located rapidly.

It is almost always better to plan to ditch parallel to the surface swell of the water, and if possible with an element of headwind.

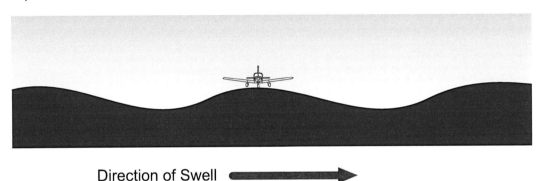

Direction of Swell ➡

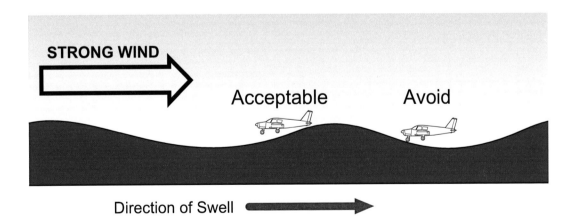

Direction of Swell ➡

After an emergency landing in a light aircraft, the priority is to evacuate the crew and passengers to a safe position upwind of the aircraft, if possible taking the fire extinguisher and first aid kit on leaving the aircraft. If time permits, all main aircraft systems (fuel, engine, electrical) should be turned off.

When flying in a single-engine aircraft over water and beyond gliding distance of land, all occupants should wear lifejackets. In the event of a ditching, lifejackets must <u>not</u> be inflated until the wearer is outside the aircraft.

Contaminated Runways

A runway is considered to be **contaminated** when more than 25% of the runway surface area being used is covered by:

- surface water more than 3mm deep (or by slush, or loose snow, equivalent to more than 3mm of water);

- compacted snow; or

- ice.

A 'wet runway' is one where the runway surface is covered with water, or equivalent, less than 3mm deep, or when there is sufficient moisture on the runway surface to cause it to appear reflective, but without significant areas of standing water.

A 'damp runway' has a surface which is not dry, but the moisture on it does not give it a shiny appearance.

A 'dry runway' is neither wet nor contaminated.

Sometimes, runway condition may be described as 'flooded', meaning that extensive patches of standing water are visible (ie more than 50% of the assessed area is covered by water more than 3mm deep).

The use of a contaminated runway should be avoided if at all possible.

EASA Private Pilot Licence
Aeroplane
Operational Procedures

Time allowed: 30 minutes

No. of questions: 16

Total Marks: 100

Instructions:

The paper consists of 16 multiple choice questions, each carries 6.25 marks. The pass mark is 75% (ie 12 questions or more must be answered correctly). Marks are not deducted for incorrect answers.

Be sure to carefully read each question and ensure that you understand it before considering the answer choices. Only one of the answers is complete and correct; the others are either incomplete, incorrect or based on a misconception.

You should indicate the correct answer by placing a cross in the appropriate box of the answer sheet. If you decide to change an answer, you should erase the original choice and put a cross in the box representing your new selection.

Each question has an average answer time of just under 2 minutes. No credit is given for unanswered questions.

Operational Procedures Practice Paper ONE

1. A runway surface that is covered with water less than 3mm deep, but without significant areas of standing water, can be described as

   (a) Flooded

   (b) Wet

   (c) Contaminated

   (d) Cleaned

2. A runway's Accelerate-Stop Distance Available (ASDA) is defined as:

   (a) The TORA plus the length of stopway

   (b) The TODA plus any Clearway

   (c) Never being greater than the TORA

   (d) Always being the same as the LDA

3. The period between the end of evening civil twilight and the beginning of morning civil twilight can be described as:

   (a) Nautical twilight

   (b) Night

   (c) Day

   (d) Dusk

4. The meaning of a flashing red light signal, sent from ATC to an aircraft on the ground is:

   (a) Stop

   (b) Permission to take-off

   (c) Move clear of the landing area

   (d) Return to the starting point on the aerodrome

5. Which of the following is the most accurate definition of the Pilot In Command?

   (a) The person who has authorised a flight

   (b) The pilot manipulating the flying controls

   (c) Always the pilot with the highest qualifications or greatest experience

   (d) The pilot designated as being in command and charged with the safe conduct of the flight

6. 'Flight Time' for an aeroplane is defined by ICAO as:

   (a) The time from engine start before flight, to engine shutdown after flight

   (b) The time from when an aircraft first moves under its own power with the purpose of taking-off, until it comes to a stop at the end of the flight

   (c) The time from take-off until landing

   (d) Airborne time plus ten minutes

7. Noise abatement procedures at an aerodrome:

   (a) Should be described in the AIP and commercial flight guides

   (b) Apply to Commercial Air Transport operations only

   (c) Apply to Turbo Jet aircraft only

   (d) Require approval by the Competent Authority

8. Which of the following situations are likely to cause the strongest wake turbulence?

(a) A light aircraft flying at cruise airspeed

(b) A light aircraft climbing after take-off

(c) A heavy aircraft flying slowly in the approach configuration

(d) A heavy aircraft flying at cruise airspeed

9. In relation to helicopters and wake turbulence:

(a) Helicopters do not produce wake turbulence

(b) Helicopters only produce wake turbulence when in forward flight

(c) Helicopters do not produce wake turbulence when 'hover taxiing'

(d) Helicopters produce more intense wake turbulence than an aeroplane of similar weight

10. If landing behind a larger aircraft, in addition to observing wake turbulence separation minima, where possible a pilot of the following aircraft should aim to:

(a) Approach below the leading aircraft's flightpath and land before its touchdown point

(b) Approach above the leading aircraft's flightpath and land beyond its touchdown point

(c) Approach below the leading aircraft's flightpath and land at its touchdown point

(d) Approach along the leading aircraft's flightpath and land before its touchdown point

11. On approach to land an aircraft encounters 'windshear', so that a 20 knot headwind component abruptly becomes a 10 knot tailwind component. In terms of aircraft airspeed:

(a) Airspeed will increase

(b) Airspeed will be unaffected

(c) Airspeed will reduce suddenly

(d) Airspeed will increase by half the windshear factor

12. An aircraft is climbing after take-off when it encounters an abrupt change from headwind to tailwind as it climbs through a marked temperature inversion. Without corrective action by the pilot, the effect on airspeed and rate of climb is likely to be:

(a) A decrease in airspeed and reduction in rate of climb

(b) An increase in airspeed and increase in rate of climb

(c) A decrease in airspeed and increase in rate of climb

(d) An increase in airspeed and reduction in rate of climb

13. An aircraft on approach flying directly into a microburst is most likely to <u>initially</u> encounter:

(a) Smooth air

(b) An increase in airspeed

(c) A decrease in airspeed

(d) An increase in rate of descent

14. For overwater flight in a single engine aircraft, lifejackets:

    (i) Should be stored in the baggage compartment

    (ii) Should be worn

    (iii) Should be carried ready to be put on in case of ditching

    (iv) Should be inflated in a ditching only once outside the aircraft

    (v) Should be inflated when the aircraft touches down

The correct statements are:

(a)   (i) & (iv)

(b)   (iii) & (iv)

(c)   (ii) & (iv)

(d)   (iii) & (v)

15. In the event of an engine failure over water, as opposed to an engine failure over land, the pilot should:

(a)   Omit the distress call altogether

(b)   Make a distress call earlier in the ditching sequence and consider using the 7700 transponder code

(c)   Aim to touchdown at a faster than normal landing speed

(d)   Aim for a tailwind touchdown whenever possible

16. In relation to holding points at a 'controlled aerodrome':

(a)   They usually incorporate solid and broken yellow lines and should only be crossed with ATC clearance

(b)   ATC clearance to cross a holding point is not required if the pilot makes a good lookout

(c)   Holding point lines on the taxiway are usually painted red

(d)   Holding points usually consist of lights only

1. The Take Off Distance Available (TODA) of a runway is defined as:
   (a) The length of the runway plus stopway
   (b) The length of the runway plus any clearway
   (c) The length of the runway only
   (d) The length of the runway minus any stopway

2. An Operations Manual can be defined as:
   (a) A manual containing procedures, instructions and guidance for use by operational personnel in the execution of their duties
   (b) Guidance material developed by an industry body
   (c) A manual associated with the certificate of airworthiness, containing limitations
   (d) A document which describes specific scheduled maintenance tasks

3. A runway may be described as 'damp' if:
   (a) It is contaminated
   (b) It has extensive areas of standing water
   (c) The moisture on the runway does not give a shiny appearance
   (d) It is neither wet nor contaminated

4. Operations from a 'contaminated' runway:
   (a) Require no special considerations
   (b) Are prohibited for General Aviation aircraft
   (c) Should be avoided whenever possible
   (d) Require specific authorisation from the Competent Authority

5. What is the meaning of a steady green light signal, sent from ATC to an aircraft in the air?
   (a) You may land
   (b) Return to aerodrome
   (c) Give way to other aircraft
   (d) Position for another runway

6. In relation to wake turbulence:
   (a) It is present anytime an aeroplane or helicopter is generating lift
   (b) It is not created by an aeroplane whilst it is on the ground
   (c) It is only generated by turbo jet aircraft
   (d) It is only a hazard in the approach phase

7. To minimise the probability of a wake turbulence encounter:
   (a) Aim to fly up to 1000ft below a larger aircraft's flight path
   (b) Cross below a larger aircraft's flightpath at 90 degrees
   (c) Avoid flying behind and below the flightpath of a larger aircraft
   (d) Make a more shallow approach if landing behind a larger aircraft

Paper TWO

8. An aircraft is established on the approach to land when it encounters 'windshear', so that a 20kt headwind component abruptly becomes a 10kt tailwind component. If the pilot takes no corrective action, the aircraft's rate of descent is likely to:

    (a) Increase

    (b) Decrease

    (c) Remain the same

    (d) Reduce by half the windshear factor

9. Which of the following statements is most accurate in relation to windshear:

    (a) It is only found around thunderstorms

    (b) It can be associated with thunderstorms, virga, microbursts, strong winds, inversions and frontal passage

    (c) It occurs in daylight hours only

    (d) It is always visible if flying in VMC

10. With regard to microbursts and downdrafts:

    (a) Downdraughts are only found under thunderstorms

    (b) Virga usually gives rise to strong updrafts

    (c) Windshear is only found directly under a thunderstorm

    (d) Both thunderstorms and virga can cause downdraughts and windshear

11. For overwater flight, in the event of a ditching passengers should be briefed to:

    (a) Only inflate lifejackets when outside the aircraft

    (b) Inflate lifejackets at the first sign of trouble

    (c) Inflate lifejackets when the aircraft touches down on the water

    (d) Inflate lifejackets when water in the cabin reaches chest height

12. In the event of a ditching in light wind conditions, the pilot should aim to touchdown:

    (a) Parallel to the swell, on a crest if possible

    (b) Directly into the swell

    (c) Into wind regardless of swell

    (d) Downwind and landing on the back of the swell

13. When evacuating an aircraft after an emergency landing, and making due allowance for circumstances and the emergency checklist:

    (i) Passengers should be evacuated to a position upwind of the aircraft

    (ii) Systems should be left on so the aircraft can be easily moved

    (iii) The first aid kit and extinguisher should be taken if possible

    (iv) The pilot must await ATC clearance before starting the evacuation

    The most correct combination of statements is:

    (a) (ii), (iii) and (iv)

    (b) (i) & (iii)

    (c) (ii), (iii) & (iv)

    (d) (ii) & (iv)

14. Although very rare, if an in-flight cabin fire does occur in a light aircraft it is most likely to be:

    (a)   Caused by some kind of electrical malfunction

    (b)   A minor abnormality, not requiring urgent action

    (c)   Not serious enough to require use of the fire extinguisher

    (d)   Capable of being extinguished by reducing airspeed

15. The most serious consequence of over-priming a piston engine during start is:

    (a)   Exhausting the aircraft battery

    (b)   Increased risk of engine fire

    (c)   Wearing out the starter motor

    (d)   Damage to the suction pump

16. At a runway holding point of a controlled aerodrome:

    (a)   An illuminated red stop bar is advisory only and may be crossed at the pilot's discretion

    (b)   Painted taxiway markings are advisory only and may be crossed at the pilot's discretion

    (c)   The pilot may cross an illuminated red stop bar and taxiway markings, provided the aircraft holds short of the runway itself

    (d)   ATC clearance is required to proceed past a runway holding point

Paper TWO

Intentionally Left Blank

1. The length of unobstructed runway that will support the aircraft during take-off is the:

   (a) Take-off Distance Available (TODA)

   (b) Accelerate Run Available (ARA)

   (c) Take-off Run Available (TORA)

   (d) Emergency Distance Available (EDA)

2. A runway condition where extensive patches of standing water are visible is described as:

   (a) Wet

   (b) Flooded

   (c) Water Patches

   (d) Damp

3. If a runway is described as 'Wet', which of the following conditions apply:

   (a) The runway surface is covered in water, but no significant patches of standing water are visible

   (b) There are significant patches of standing water

   (c) The runway surface shows a change of colour due to moisture

   (d) There is more than 25% coverage of ice or loose snow

4. In relation to a 'contaminated' runway, which of the following statements is most accurate:

   (a) Operations from contaminated runways are prohibited

   (b) Operations from contaminated runways require no specific performance considerations

   (c) Operations from contaminated runways should be avoided

   (d) Operations from contaminated runways require specific authorisation from ICAO

5. A situation where a pilot is required to make an unavoidable landing (or ditching) is best described as:

   (a) An engine failure

   (b) A diversion

   (c) A forced landing

   (d) A precision landing

6. 'General Aviation Operation' is defined by ICAO as being:

   (a) Operation of aircraft with a mass of less than 5700kg

   (b) Any operation of civil aircraft

   (c) Any operation of aircraft by the holder of a non-commercial licence

   (d) Aircraft operation other than Commercial Air Transport or Aerial Work

7. An aircraft is established on the approach to land when it encounters 'windshear', so that a 10 knot tailwind component abruptly becomes a 20 knot headwind component. If the pilot takes no corrective action, in respect of the aircraft's airspeed and rate of descent:

    (a)   Airspeed will increase, rate of descent will decrease

    (b)   Airspeed will increase, rate of descent will increase

    (c)   Airspeed will decrease, rate of descent will increase

    (d)   Airspeed will decrease, rate of descent will decrease

8. To minimise the danger of a wake turbulence encounter, the pilot of an aeroplane operating in the vicinity of a helicopter hover taxiing, should:

    (a)   Observe a minimum separation of 30 feet

    (b)   Not find it necessary to observe any minimum separation

    (c)   Should aim to follow closely behind the helicopter, to stay in-between the vortices

    (d)   Should avoid operating at less than the equivalent of three rotor blade diameters

9. Which of the following statements about wake turbulence is most accurate:

    (a)   It may be most dangerous in light cross wind conditions

    (b)   It is most dangerous in strong wind conditions

    (c)   Vortices tend to drift up above the generating aircraft's flight path

    (d)   Vortices tend to move inwards and converge

10. For overwater flight in a single engine aircraft:
    (i) The pilot should wear a lifejacket
    (ii) Passengers should wear inflated lifejackets
    (iii) Passenger lifejackets should be worn but not inflated inside the aircraft
    (iv) Passenger lifejackets should be carried but not worn until outside the aircraft
    (v) The pilot only should inflate his lifejacket before ditching

    The correct statements are:

    (a)   (i) & (iv)

    (b)   (iii) & (v)

    (c)   (ii) & (iv)

    (d)   (i) & (iii)

11. When considering the most appropriate actions in a ditching scenario, and making due allowance for circumstances and the emergency checklist:
    (i) Gliding should be done at maximum endurance glide speed if outside range of land
    (ii) The distress call should be made early
    (iii) The transponder should be turned off
    (iv) Head towards shipping if too far from land
    (v) Land into a strong wind

    The most correct statements, in sequence are:

    (a)   (i), (ii), (iv) and (v)

    (b)   (ii), (iii), (iv)

    (c)   (ii), (iii) & (iv)

    (d)   (ii), (iii) & (v)

12. By ICAO definition, a manual, associated with the Certificate of Airworthiness, containing limitations within which the aircraft is to be considered airworthy, and instructions and information necessary for the flight crew members for the safe operation of the aircraft is:

(a)   An operations manual

(b)   A Safety Management Manual (SMS)

(c)   A Flight Manual or Pilot Operating Handbook

(d)   A Training Manual

13. In the event of an engine failure in the cruise, at the appropriate point in the sequence and subject to the emergency checklist, a general guide to causes of failure to be checked and subsequent action might best include:

(a)   Shut down all engine systems, then attempt re-start

(b)   Shut down all aircraft systems, then use normal engine start checklist

(c)   Check fuel controls (eg selector, mixture, fuel pump), carburettor heat/induction air and ignition system, if appropriate attempt re-start

(d)   Do not attempt re-start if the propeller is stationary

14. In the event of smoke in the cockpit during flight, accompanied by an 'acrid' smell:

(a)   Suspect electrical fire. Shut down electrical system, divert or forced landing as appropriate, use fire extinguisher if smoke persists

(b)   Suspect suction gauge failure. Continue flight

(c)   Suspect hydraulic leak, check brake fluid contents on landing

(d)   Inform ATC, await ATC instructions before further action

15. In relation to a holding point at a 'controlled aerodrome':

(a)   It is permissible to cross illuminated red 'stop bar' lights if a good lookout is made

(b)   Do not taxi across illuminated red 'stop bar' lights

(c)   Red stop lights are advisory only

(d)   The 'stop bar' shows red when it is clear to pass the holding point

16. Although rare, an engine fire on start in a light aircraft is most likely to be caused by:

(a)   A malfunctioning suction pump

(b)   Failure of one of the magnetos or ignition systems

(c)   An overheating starter motor

(d)   'Over-priming' of the engine

Operational Procedures paper 1 Q1 Answer B

A 'wet runway' is one where the runway surface is covered with water, or equivalent, less than 3mm deep, or when there is sufficient moisture on the runway surface to cause it to appear reflective, but without significant areas of standing water.

Further Reference: PPL2 Air Law > Rules of the Air > Runways

Operational Procedures paper 1 Q2 Answer A

The accelerate-stop distance available (ASDA) is defined as the length of the take-off run available (TORA) plus the length of stopway.

The take-off run available (TORA) is the length of runway suitable for the ground run of an aeroplane taking off.

The stopway is an area beyond the runway which can be safely used for stopping an aircraft in the event of an aborted take-off.

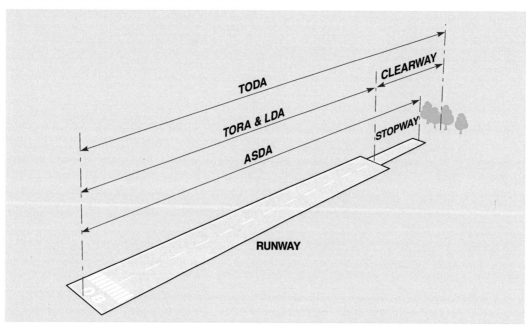

Further reference: PPL2 Air Law > Rules of the Air > Runways

Operational Procedures paper 1 Q3 Answer B

'Night' means the hours between the end of evening civil twilight and the beginning of morning civil twilight. Civil twilight ends in the evening when the centre of the sun's disc is 6 degrees below the horizon and begins in the morning when the centre of the sun's disc is 6 degrees below the horizon.

In the UK, for licencing purposes night is defined as the period from half an hour after sunset to half an hour before sunrise.

Further Reference: PPL2 Air Law > JAA/EASA Regulations > Private Pilot Licence
                     (Aeroplane)

Operational Procedures paper 1 Q4 Answer C

The following table summarises the light signals from an ATC unit to an aircraft:

ATC Light Signals to Aircraft on Ground

STOP	STOP
GET OFF GET OFF	Move clear of runway
GO	You may take-off
OK TAXI OK TAXI	OK to Taxi
COME BACK COME BACK	Return to starting point

ATC Light Signals to Aircraft in the Air

NO	Give way and continue circling
GO AWAY GO AWAY	Do not land here
LAND	You may land
COME BACK COME BACK	Return to this airfield
LAND HERE LAND HERE	Land at this airfield

Further Reference: PPL2 Air Law > Rules of the Air > Light Signals

Operational Procedures paper 1 Q5 Answer D

By ICAO and EASA definition, the pilot-in-command' means the pilot designated by the operator, or in the case of general aviation, the owner, as being in command and charged with the safe conduct of a flight.

Further Reference: PPL2 Operational Procedures > Operation of Aircraft > Operation of Aircraft

Operational Procedures paper 1 Q6 Answer B

By ICAO definition, flight time for an aeroplane is the time from when an aircraft first moves under its own power with the purpose of taking-off, until it comes to a rest at the end of the flight.

Further Reference: PPL2 Operational Procedures > Operation of Aircraft > Operation of Aircraft

Operational Procedures paper 1 Q7 Answer A

Many airfields, including those not listed in an AIP, have specific noise abatement procedures – usually in the form or routings to be followed in the vicinity of the aerodrome and specific areas to avoid. Unless otherwise stated, these procedures normally apply to all aircraft.

Further Reference: PPL2 Operational Procedures > Noise Abatement > Take-off, Approach and Landing

Operational Procedures paper 1 Q 8 Answer C

As a general rule of thumb, the heavier the aircraft and the more slowly it is flying, the stronger the wake turbulence that it will generate.

Further Reference: PPL2 Air Law > Rules of the Air and Air Traffic Services > Wake Turbulence

Answers ONE

Operational Procedures paper 1 Q9 Answer D

Studies have shown that helicopters produce more intense wake turbulence than 'fixed wing' aeroplanes of a similar weight. The wake turbulence produced by a helicopter is particularly strong during hover taxiing, the initial acceleration into forward flight and during the landing 'flare'.

Further Reference: PPL2 Air Law > Rules of the Air and Air Traffic Services > Wake Turbulence

Operational Procedures paper 1 Q10 Answer B

The general rule of wake turbulence avoidance, in addition to observing separation minima, is to stay above the leading aircraft's flightpath and on landing, if possible, land well beyond the leading aircraft's touchdown point.

Further Reference: PPL2 Air Law > Rules of the Air and Air Traffic Services > Wake Turbulence

Operational Procedures paper 1 Q11 Answer C

Windshear is caused by a sudden change in wind velocity over a small horizontal or vertical distance. In the example given in the question, if the aircraft had an airspeed of 80 knots, whilst experiencing the 20 knot headwind it's groundspeed would be 60 knots (80 – 60). When the abrupt change in wind velocity occurs, the effect of inertia means that groundspeed remains close to 60 knots, but the 10 knots tailwind means that the airspeed is now just 50 knots (60 – 10).

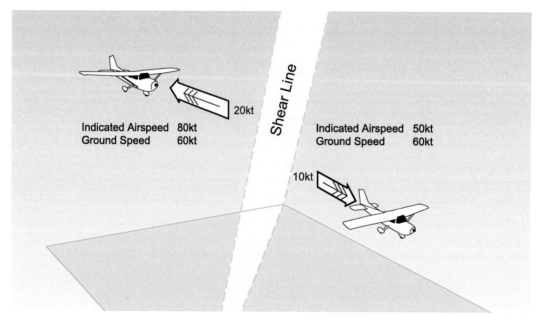

Operational Procedures paper 1 Q12 Answer A

Where a headwind component abruptly changes to a tailwind component, a loss of airspeed is likely if no corrective action is taken. This loss of airspeed is also likely to lead to a reduction in rate of climb or even to the aircraft beginning to descend.

Further Reference: PPL3 Meteorology > Flight Over Mountainous Areas and Other Weather Hazards > Windshear

Operational Procedures paper 1 Q13 Answer B

In the very specific circumstances given in the question, and aircraft on approach flying directly into a microburst is most likely to encounter a strong increase in headwind component as the massive downdraft of the microburst hits the surface and spreads outwards.

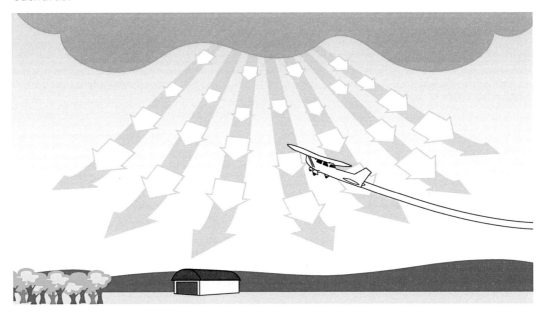

The abrupt increase in headwind component is likely to lead initially to an increase in airspeed (and probably reduction in rate of descent), at least until the aircraft flies further into the microburst and downdraught when tailwinds, loss of airspeed and dramatic increase in rate of descent are possible.

Further Reference: PPL3 Meteorology > Thunderstorms > Hazards for Aircraft

Operational Procedures paper 1 Q14 Answer C

It is strongly recommended that lifejackets are worn (but not inflated) by all occupants of a single engine aircraft flying overwater. The passengers must be briefed that, in the event of a ditching, they must not inflate their lifejacket until they are outside the aircraft.

Further Reference: PPL1 Flying Training > Exercise 16 – Forced landing Without
                      Power > Ditching
                      And
                      PPL1 Human Factors > Safety and Survival Equipment > Basics
                      of Survival

AOperational Procedures paper 1 Q15 Answer B

In the event of an engine failure over the water, beyond gliding distance of land, the distress call and possible use of the emergency transponder code should be considered earlier in the ditching sequence. This is to give the best chance of having the distress call heard (or the emergency squawk seen) before the aircraft descends too low.

In a ditching situation, quick location by search and rescue services is a prime factor in the probability of survival.

Further Reference: PPL1 Flying Training > Exercise 16 – Forced landing Without
                      Power > Ditching

Operational Procedures paper 1 Q16 Answer A

Holding points at a 'controlled aerodrome' should only be crossed after receiving (and reading back) a specific ATC clearance, and even then only after making a good visual lookout before proceeding to cross the line. Holding point markings normally consist of solid and broken yellow lines painted at right angles across the taxiway, at major airfields these lines may be supplemented by lighting.

Further Reference: PPL1 Flying Training > Exercise 5 – Taxying > Apron and
                      Manoeuvring Area Markings

Answers ONE

Operational Procedures paper 2 Q1 Answer B

ICAO annex 14 (Aerodromes) sets out the definitions of the various runway distances (sometimes referred to as 'declared distances'), and these definition are summarised in the Essential Revision section.

Further Reference: PPL2 Air Law > Rules of the Air > Runways

Operational Procedures paper 2 Q2 Answer A

By ICAO definition, an Operations Manual is a manual containing procedures, instructions and guidance for use by operational personnel in the execution of their duties. In practical terms, it is a manual produced by an operator relating to operation of the operator's aircraft.

Further Reference: PPL2 Operational Procedures > Operation of Aircraft > Operation of Aircraft

Operational Procedures paper 2 Q3 Answer C

A 'damp' runway has a surface which is not dry, but the moisture on it does not give it a shiny appearance.

Further Reference: PPL2 Air Law > Rules of the Air > Runways

Operational Procedures paper 2 Q4 Answer C

The UK CAA recommend that the use of a contaminated runway should be avoided if at all possible. Further, if extensive areas of standing water, slush or wet snow are present and there is doubt about the depth, take-off should not be attempted.

Further Reference: PPL2 Air Law > Rules of the Air > Runways

Operational Procedures paper 2 Q5 Answer A

The table summarising the light signals from an ATC unit to an aircraft is found in the Essential Revision section.

Further Reference: PPL2 Air Law > Rules of the Air > Light Signals

Operational Procedures paper 2 Q6 Answer A

Wake turbulence is a result of the creation of lift – anytime an aeroplane's wing or a helicopter's rotor blades are creating lift, some wake turbulence in being generated.

Further Reference: PPL2 Air Law > Rules of the Air and Air Traffic Services > Wake Turbulence

Operational Procedures paper 2 Q7 Answer C

In addition to applying wake turbulence separation minima, positioning or aircraft to be above and if possible upwind of a leading aircraft's flightpath will reduce the chances of a wake turbulence encounter.

Further Reference: PPL2 Air Law > Rules of the Air and Air Traffic Services > Wake Turbulence

Operational Procedures paper 2 Q8 Answer A

Windshear is caused by a sudden change in wind velocity over a small horizontal or vertical distance. In the example given in the question, the abrupt change in wind velocity (from headwind to tailwind) will lead to a reduction in airspeed if no corrective action is taken.

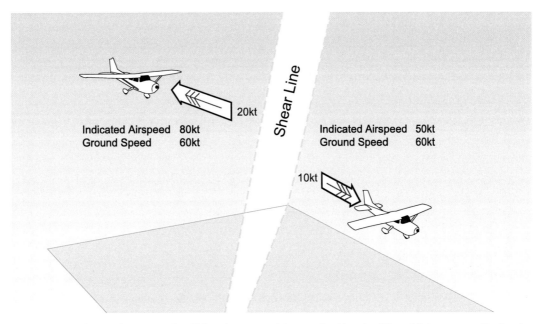

This abrupt loss of airspeed will lead to a sudden reduction in lift, which means that rate of descent is likely to increase suddenly.

Further Reference: PPL3 Meteorology > Flight Over Mountainous Areas and Other Weather Hazards > Windshear

Operational Procedures paper 2 Q9 Answer B

Windshear can be associated with:

Thunderstorms and microbursts,

Strong Winds,

Marked temperature inversions,

Passage of a front,

Virga.

Except in exception circumstances (for example 'roll cloud', on the gust front ahead of a thunderstorm, or heavy precipitation in a microburst), areas of windshear are not normally visible and, as with the weather phenomena it is associated with, windshear can occur at any time of night or day.

Further Reference: PPL3 Meteorology > Flight Over Mountainous Areas and Other Weather Hazards > Windshear
And
PPL3 Meteorology > Thunderstorms > Hazards for Aircraft

Operational Procedures paper 2 Q10 Answer D

Strong downdraughts (including microbursts) can be found in association with both thunderstorms and virga. The windshear associated with a thunderstorm may be found at considerable distances (eg up to 20 miles) from the thunderstorm, for example on the 'gust front' ahead of a thunderstorm.

Further Reference: PPL3 Meteorology > Thunderstorms > Hazards for Aircraft

Answers TWO

Operational Procedures paper 2 Q11 Answer A

When lifejackets are worn in an aircraft (as is strongly recommended for overwater flight in a single engine aircraft), the passengers must be briefed that, in the event of a ditching, they must not inflate their lifejacket until they are outside the aircraft (and clear from under the wing if exiting a high-wing aircraft).

This briefing is essential as a lifejacket inflated inside the cockpit will not only impeded exit from the aircraft but will also increase the risk of the lifejacket chambers becoming punctured.

Further Reference: PPL1 Flying Training > Exercise 16 – Forced landing Without Power > Ditching
And
PPL1 Human Factors > Safety and Survival Equipment > Basics of Survival

Operational Procedures paper 2 Q12 Answer A

Except in very strong wind conditions (eg 35 knots or more), in the event of ditching it is recommended to aim to land parallel to the swell (the surface undulation of the sea), and if possible on the crest of the swell. It may be possible to do this whilst also approaching into an element of headwind, but it is the touchdown in relation to the surface swell which is of utmost importance.

Further Reference: PPL1 Flying Training > Exercise 16 Forced landing without power > Ditching

Operational Procedures paper 2 Q13 Answer B

In any emergency situation, the pilot must decide what actions are appropriate in the particular circumstances, in conjunction with the use of the emergency checklist. It is almost always the case that all aircraft system should be shut down and the passengers evacuated to a safe distance upwind of the aircraft (to be clear of any smoke or flames). If possible, the fire extinguisher and fire aid kit should be taken during the evacuation so that they are available if needed.

Further Reference: PPL1 Flying Training > Exercise 16 – Forced landing Without Power > Actions After Landing

Operational Procedures paper 2 Q14 Answer A

Any guide to actions in an emergency situation are, by their nature, guidance only and must be applied in accordance with the actual emergency circumstances and the aircraft's emergency checklist.

Although very rare, when in-flight cabin fires do occur they are most often associated with some type of electrical failure and require immediate action by the pilot.

Further Reference: PPL1 Flying Training > Exercise 1e Aircraft Familiarisation > Cabin Fire in the Air

Operational Procedures paper 2 Q15 Answer B

'Over-priming' the engine during start, either by over-use of the priming control, or by 'pumping' the throttle of an engine which has an 'accelerator' pump, is a common cause of an engine fires on start.

Further Reference: PPL1 Flying Training > Exercise 2 Preparation for flight and action after flight > Starting Problems

Operational Procedures paper 2 Q16 Answer D

At a controlled aerodrome (where Air Traffic Control is in operation), a runway holding point may only be passed with ATC clearance, and even then only after making a good lookout for aircraft on, or approaching, the runway.

Even with ATC clearance, it is not permissible to pass an illuminated red stop bar.

Further Reference: PPL2 Air Law > Rules of the Air > Taxiway Signals and Markings

Operational Procedures paper 3 Q1 Answer C

The definitions of the various runway 'declared distances' are summarised in the Essential Revision section.

Further Reference: PPL2 Air Law > Rules of the Air > Runways

Operational Procedures paper 3 Q2 Answer B

A runway may be described as 'flooded' when extensive patches of standing water are visible (ie more than 50% of the assessed area is covered by water more than 3mm deep).

Further Reference: PPL2 Air Law > Rules of the Air > Runways

Operational Procedures paper 3 Q3 Answer A

By ICAO definition, a runway is 'wet' if the surface is soaked but there is no extensive standing water.

Further Reference: PPL2 Air Law > Rules of the Air > Runways

Operational Procedures paper 3 Q4 Answer C

The UK CAA recommend that the use of a contaminated runway should be avoided if at all possible. Further, if extensive areas of standing water, slush or wet snow are present and there is doubt about the depth, take-off should not be attempted.

Further Reference: PPL2 Air Law > Rules of the Air > Runways

Operational Procedures paper 3 Q5 Answer C

A forced landing is a situation where a pilot is required to make an unavoidable landing (or ditching) and there can be a reasonable expectation of no injuries to those in the aircraft or on the surface.

Further Reference: PPL1 Flying Training > Exercise 16 Forced landing without power
                     and
                     PPL1 Flying Training > Exercise 17 The precautionary landing

Operational Procedures paper 3 Q6 Answer D

By ICAO definition, 'General Aviation Operation' is an aircraft operation other than Commercial Air Transport operation or Aerial Work Operation.

Further Reference: PPL2 Operational Procedures > Operation of Aircraft > Operation of Aircraft

Operational Procedures paper 3 Q7 Answer A

In the example given in the question, the abrupt change in wind velocity (from tailwind to headwind) will lead to a sudden increase in airspeed if no corrective action is taken.

This sudden increase in airspeed will lead to an increase in lift, which means that rate of descent is likely to reduce; the aircraft may even begin to climb.

Over time the aircraft would settle back to the trimmed airspeed and rate of descent, but when at low level, prompt pilot action (usually in the form of a go-around) is required if encountering windshear of this magnitude.

Further Reference: PPL3 Meteorology > Flight Over Mountainous Areas and Other
                     Weather Hazards > Windshear

Operational Procedures paper 3 Q8 Answer D

Studies suggest that aeroplanes should avoid helicopters in flight by a distance equivalent to at least three rotor diameters of the helicopter.

Further Reference: PPL2 Air Law > Rules of the Air and Air Traffic Services > Wake
                     Turbulence

AOperational Procedures paper 3 Q9 Answer A

The wing tip vortices that generate wake turbulence tend to drift down and outwards from the wing tips. In a light cross wind, a vortex may stay over a runway, rather than drifting away from it.

Further Reference: PPL2 Air Law > Rules of the Air and Air Traffic Services > Wake Turbulence

Operational Procedures paper 3 Q10 Answer D

All occupants of a single engine aircraft flying overwater should wear (but not inflate) lifejackets. The passengers must be briefed that, in the event of a ditching, they must not inflate their lifejacket until they are outside the aircraft.

Further Reference: PPL1 Flying Training > Exercise 16 – Forced landing Without Power > Ditching
And
PPL1 Human Factors > Safety and Survival Equipment > Basics of Survival

Operational Procedures paper 3 Q11 Answer A

In the event of an engine failure over the water, beyond gliding distance of land, a general guide to the sequence of actions includes:

■ Establishing glide at the 'maximum endurance glide airspeed' to maximise airborne time;

■ Make an early distress call;

■ Use the transponder as appropriate (either by ATC instruction or squawk 7700 if no ATC code selected);

■ Head towards any shipping in the area, as a general rule land ahead or alongside a ship, not behind it;

■ In strong wind conditions, aim to touchdown into the wind, at the slowest safe landing speed.

Further Reference: PPL1 Flying Training > Exercise 16 – Forced landing Without Power > Ditching

Operational Procedures paper 3 Q12 Answer C

By ICAO definition, a manual associated with the Certificate of Airworthiness, containing limitations within which the aircraft is to be considered airworthy, and instructions and information necessary for the flight crew members for the safe operation of the aircraft is a Flight Manual (FM), also known as a Pilots Operating handbook (POH).

Further Reference: PPL2 Air Law > Airworthiness of Aircraft > Aircraft Limits and Information

Operational Procedures paper 3 Q13 Answer C

Any guide to actions in an emergency situation are, by their nature, guidance only and must be applied in accordance with the actual emergency circumstances and the aircraft's emergency checklist.

As a general rule, the main items to check in the event of an unexplained engine failure at altitude follow the most common causes of engine failure:

Fuel: check the fuel selector, fuel pump and mixture control as appropriate.

Carburettor heat or Induction air control: select 'HOT' or 'ON' as appropriate.

Ignition Controls: Check the ignition controls/switches, attempt re-start if appropriate.

Further Reference: PPL1 Flying Training > Exercise 16 Forced landing without power > Check for Cause of Failure

Operational Procedures paper 3 Q14 Answer A

Any guide to actions in an emergency situation are, by their nature, guidance only and must be applied in accordance with the actual emergency circumstances and the aircraft's emergency checklist.

Although very rare, when in-flight cabin fires do occur they are most often associated with some type of electrical failure. If the suspect device can be immediately identified (for example, smoke appears after turning on a particular electrical device), then switch it off and if possible 'pop' the appropriate fuse or circuit breaker. Otherwise close down the electrical system using the master switch and make an immediate diversion or forced landing as circumstances dictate.

If the fire persists and location can be identified, use the aircraft hand-held fire extinguisher without delay.

Further Reference: PPL1 Flying Training > Exercise 1e Aircraft Familiarisation > Cabin Fire in the Air

Operational Procedures paper 3 Q15 Answer B

Red 'stop bar' lights are found at the holding points of many major 'controlled aerodromes'. They should not be crossed whilst they are illuminated.

Further Reference: PPL1 Flying Training > Exercise 5 – Taxying > Apron and Manoeuvring Area Markings

Operational Procedures paper 3 Q16 Answer D

An engine fire on engine start is most often caused by 'over-priming' the engine. This can be done either by over-use of the priming control, or by 'pumping' the throttle of an engine which has an 'accelerator' pump. In any event, over-priming can lead to fuel pooling within the induction system or under the engine, leading to a risk of an engine fire.

Further Reference: PPL1 Flying Training > Exercise 2 Preparation for flight and action after flight > Starting Problems

Intentionally Left Blank

	Paper 1					Paper 2					Paper 3			
	A	B	C	D		A	B	C	D		A	B	C	D
1	☐	☐	☐	☐	1	☐	☐	☐	☐	1	☐	☐	☐	☐
2	☐	☐	☐	☐	2	☐	☐	☐	☐	2	☐	☐	☐	☐
3	☐	☐	☐	☐	3	☐	☐	☐	☐	3	☐	☐	☐	☐
4	☐	☐	☐	☐	4	☐	☐	☐	☐	4	☐	☐	☐	☐
5	☐	☐	☐	☐	5	☐	☐	☐	☐	5	☐	☐	☐	☐
6	☐	☐	☐	☐	6	☐	☐	☐	☐	6	☐	☐	☐	☐
7	☐	☐	☐	☐	7	☐	☐	☐	☐	7	☐	☐	☐	☐
8	☐	☐	☐	☐	8	☐	☐	☐	☐	8	☐	☐	☐	☐
9	☐	☐	☐	☐	9	☐	☐	☐	☐	9	☐	☐	☐	☐
10	☐	☐	☐	☐	10	☐	☐	☐	☐	10	☐	☐	☐	☐
11	☐	☐	☐	☐	11	☐	☐	☐	☐	11	☐	☐	☐	☐
12	☐	☐	☐	☐	12	☐	☐	☐	☐	12	☐	☐	☐	☐
13	☐	☐	☐	☐	13	☐	☐	☐	☐	13	☐	☐	☐	☐
14	☐	☐	☐	☐	14	☐	☐	☐	☐	14	☐	☐	☐	☐
15	☐	☐	☐	☐	15	☐	☐	☐	☐	15	☐	☐	☐	☐
16	☐	☐	☐	☐	16	☐	☐	☐	☐	16	☐	☐	☐	☐

Answers

Intentionally Left Blank